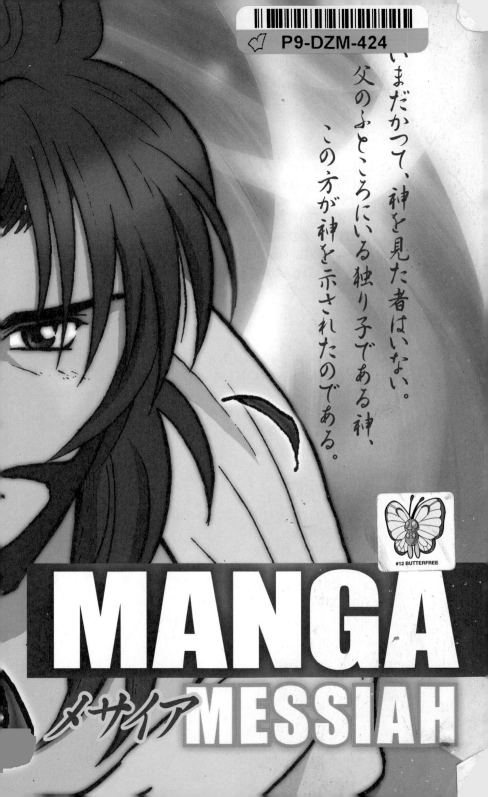

Contents

Chapter

Chapter

Chapter

Chapter I

IN THE TIME OF HEROD, KING OF JUDEA...

NAZARETH, A TOWN IN GALILEE LOCATED ABOUT 60 MILES NORTH OF JERUSALEM...

YOSEF !!

YOU'VE BEEN WORKING SO **HARD** ALL DAY!

I'VE **BROUGHT** SOMETHING FOR **YOU!**

THANK YOU, MIRYAM!

MIRYAM WAS JUST A YOUNG TEENAGER ENGAGED TO A CARPENTER NAMED YOSEF...

YOU'VE WORKED **ALL** THE WAY UNTIL **EVENING,** YOSEF!

SEE? THERE ARE **STARS** IN THE SKY!

YES, THEY'RE **BEAUTIFUL,** MIRYAM...

WELL, WE'D BETTER GO HOME... **GOOD NIGHT!**

1. THE BIRTH OF YESHUAH

THE HOLY SPIRIT WILL COME TO YOU ... THE POWER OF THE MOST HIGH GOD WILL COVER YOU!

THE HOLY ONE BORN TO YOU WILL BE CALLED THE SON OF GOD!

I ALSO HAVE NEWS ABOUT YOUR RELATIVE ELIZABETH, MIRYAM...

ELIZA-BETH?

SHE IS OLD... BUT SHE, TOO, IS GOING TO HAVE A SON!

PEOPLE THOUGHT SHE COULDN'T HAVE CHILDREN... BUT NOW SHE IS SIX MONTHS PREGNANT!

... BECAUSE NOTHING IS IMPOSSIBLE WITH GOD!

....

I SERVE THE LORD ... MAY EVERYTHING HAPPEN TO ME JUST AS YOU SAY IT WILL!

FWOO

Matthew 1:18-25

WHEN YOSEF AWOKE, HE DID WHAT THE ANGEL OF THE LORD HAD COMMANDED HIM TO DO... HE TOOK MIRYAM HOME AS HIS WIFE...

!!

IMMANUEL...

THAT... THAT NAME MEANS "GOD IS WITH US!"

THE BABY INSIDE MIRYAM IS THE SON OF GOD... BRINGING US SALVATION!

... BUT HE DID NOT SLEEP WITH HER UNTIL AFTER SHE HAD GIVEN BIRTH TO HER FIRSTBORN SON!

ARE YOU ALL RIGHT, MIRYAM?

YES, THANKS, YOSEF!

YES, BUT I GUESS WE HAVE NO CHOICE... WE MUST GO TO BETHLEHEM BECAUSE WE BOTH BELONG TO THE FAMILY OF DAVID!

... AND I AM SO HAPPY TO REGISTER WITH YOU AS YOUR WIFE!

IT'S SO DIFFICULT TO MAKE THE TRIP BACK TO OUR HOMETOWN WHILE YOU'RE PREGNANT!

THIS WILL BE A **LONG** TRIP FROM **NAZARETH** IN GALILEE TO **BETHLEHEM** IN JUDEA, MIRYAM...

IN THOSE DAYS, CAESAR AUGUSTUS HAD MADE A LAW... IT REQUIRED THAT A LIST BE MADE OF EVERYONE IN THE WHOLE ROMAN WORLD!

THIS WAS CALLED A "REGISTRATION OF RESIDENCE."

... AND I'M **WORRIED** ABOUT WHETHER YOU CAN **TRAVEL** IN YOUR CONDITION!

ISRAEL

NAZARETH

JERUSALEM

BETHLEHEM

DEAD SEA

EGYPT

Smile

... IF I'M WITH **YOU!**

I'LL BE OKAY...

UHH... BY THE WAY, MIRYAM...

I'D LIKE TO **HEAR** ABOUT THE TIME YOU SPENT VISITING WITH **ELIZABETH**...

I'M SURE THERE'S A **LOT** TO TELL SINCE YOU WERE THERE FOR **SEVERAL** MONTHS!

YES, THER IS...

WE HAD SUCH A **WONDERFUL** TIME TALKING TOGETHER SINCE WE WERE **BOTH** PREGNANT...

I WONDER WHY HE DOESN'T *SAY* SOMETHING?

IT WAS BECAUSE ZECHARIAH THE PRIEST, HUSBAND OF ELIZABETH, COULDN'T SPEAK AT THIS TIME!

OVER 6 MONTHS EARLIER, WHILE HE WAS PERFORMING HIS PRIESTLY DUTIES, AN ANGEL HAD APPEARED TO ZECHARIAH, JUST AS HE HAD TO MIRYAM AND YOSEF ... AND FROM THAT TIME ON ZECHARIAH COULD NOT SAY A WORD!

GABRIEL ANNOUNCED TO ZECHARIAH THAT HE AND ELIZABETH WOULD FINALLY HAVE WHAT THEY HAD ALWAYS WANTED...

DON'T BE AFRAID, ZECHARIAH...

YOUR PRAYER HAS BEEN HEARD!

YOUR WIFE ELIZABETH WILL HAVE A MALE CHILD...

HE WILL BE A DELIGHT TO YOU AND IMPORTANT IN THE LORD'S EYES!

YOU MUST NAME HIM JOHN!

THIS SPECIAL CHILD WHO WAS GIVEN TO ZECHARIAH AND ELIZABETH...

... WOULD BE KNOWN AS "JOHN THE BAPTIZER" WHE HE GREW UP!

ONWARD!

TO THE PLACE WHERE THE STAR LEADS US!

FOLLOWING THE STAR, THE WISE MEN CAME TO JERUSALEM, THE CAPITAL CITY... BUT WHEN THEY DID...

... THEY MADE A DISASTROUS ASSUMPTION ABOUT WHERE THEY MIGHT FIND THE ONE THEY SOUGHT!

WOW!

TRUMP

TRUMP

WHAT AN AMAZING PROCESSION !!!

IS *THIS* THE PALACE OF *KING HEROD*?

YES, IT IS!

AH! OF *COURSE!* THE ONE WE SEEK IS PART OF THE CURRENT *ROYAL FAMILY*... HERE IN *THIS* VERY PLACE!

THAT MAKES *SENSE!* THE GREAT PRINCE IS *KING HEROD'S* OWN SON!

GET UP! TAKE THE CHILD AND HIS MOTHER AND ESCAPE TO EGYPT!

STAY THERE UNTIL I TELL YOU TO COME BACK!

HEROD IS GOING TO SEARCH FOR THE CHILD... HE WANTS TO KILL HIM!

WH-WHAT ?!

HURRY, MIRYAM! BRING YESHUAH AND BE QUICK!!

O-OKAY ...!

THOSE WISE MEN HAVE BEEN GONE TOO LONG!

I GAVE THEM A **DIRECT COMMAND** TO REPORT TO ME ABOUT THE CHILD... BUT THEY'RE **NOT** COMING BACK!

2. GROWTH OF YESHUAH

LATER, HEROD DIED...

... AND THE ANGEL APPEARED TO YOSEF AGAIN AND TOLD HIM:

"THOSE WHO WERE TRYING TO KILL THE CHILD ARE NOW DEAD!"

I HEAR THAT ARCHELAUS IS RULING IN PLACE OF HIS FATHER HEROD!

HE'S CRUEL... JUST AS HIS FATHER WAS!

I THINK IT'S TOO DANGEROUS FOR US TO GO BACK TO BETHLEHEM !!

"PERHAPS IT WOULD BE BEST TO AVOID THE WHOLE SOUTHERN REGION... AND LIVE IN NAZARETH AGAIN!"

NAZARETH

JERUSALEM

BETHLEHEM

DEAD SEA

EGYPT

SO YOSEF RESUMED HIS WORK AS A CARPENTER IN THE TOWN OF NAZARETH...

BANG

BANG

... AND THE BOY YESHUAH...

2 YEARS OLD

4 YEARS OLD

7 YEARS OLD

... GREW AND BECAME STRONG! HE WAS VERY WISE AND BLESSED BY GOD'S GRACE!

10 YEARS OLD

TEN YEARS AFTER LEAVING EGYPT, IN JERUSALEM...

YEAH, BECAUSE IT'S *SPRING* AND...

WELL, ONCE AGAIN *EVERYONE* AND THEIR UNCLE ARE *HERE* IN THE CITY!

Matthew 2:19-23   Luke 2:39,40   **41**

YESHUAH ?!
YESHUAH ?!!
LOOK !!!
!!
THERE HE IS... OUR SON, YESHUAH...
...SITTING IN THE MIDDLE OF ALL THOSE TEACHERS... TALKING WITH THEM !!
EXCUSE ME, LADY... ARE YOU THE MOTHER OF THAT BOY?
WOW! LET ME TELL YOU, THAT IS ONE BRIGHT KID YOU GOT THERE!
WHAT !!?

THE FATHER THAT YESHUAH MEANT WAS HIS FATHER GOD...

... BUT HIS PARENTS DID NOT COMPLETELY UNDERSTAND HIM AT THAT TIME!

.....

MY SON IS DEFINITELY... *DIFFERENT*... FROM THE OTHER CHILDREN!

BUT I'LL KEEP *ALL* THIS TO MYSELF... STORE IT AWAY IN MY *HEART*...

...AND JUST *OBEY THE LORD* BY RAISING HIM UP!

YESHUAH ALREADY KNEW THAT GOD WAS HIS FATHER IN A VERY SPECIAL WAY...

... BUT HE OBEYED HIS EARTHLY PARENTS AS HE GREW UP!

TURN YOUR BACK ON SIN... STOP DOING ANYTHING YOU DO THAT SEPARATES YOU FROM GOD...

HIS HEAVENLY KINGDOM IS VERY NEAR!!!

...AND START DOING THINGS THAT SHOW YOU HAVE CHANGED YOUR EVIL WAYS!

DON'T YOU DARE THINK YOU'RE SAFE IN SAYING, "ABRAHAM IS OUR FATHER! WE ARE GOD'S CHOSEN PEOPLE"!!

GOD CAN RAISE UP CHILDREN FOR ABRAHAM OUT OF ROCKS!!!

"A VOICE IS CRYING IN THE DESERT: 'PREPARE THE WAY FOR THE LORD! MAKE ALL YOUR BENT PATHS STRAIGHT FOR HIM!'"

LISTEN! NOW HE'S QUOTING FROM THE SCROLL OF THE PROPHET ISAIAH!

"BACK IN THE FIFTEENTH YEAR OF TIBERIUS CAESAR'S REIGN..."

WOW! SO, WHO IS THIS GUY WITH THE CLOTHES MADE OUT OF CAMEL HAIR AND THE LEATHER WAIST BELT?

"THE BIRTH OF JOHN, SON OF ZECHARIAH AND ELIZABETH...

... HAD BEEN ANNOUNCED TO THEM BY AN ANGEL FROM HEAVEN!"

THAT WILD MAN IN THE WATER? WHY, HE'S JOHN THE BAPTIZER! HE'S BAPTIZING PEOPLE HERE IN OUR JORDAN RIVER!

I AM ONLY **PREPARING** THE WAY FOR THE ONE WHO WILL BE ARRIVING **AFTER** ME...

... AND HE IS COMING **SOON!**

IN FACT... THE LORD TOLD ME HE **ALREADY** STANDS AMONG US... BUT WE DON'T **KNOW** HIM!

BUT I **DO** KNOW HE IS **MUCH** MORE POWERFUL THAN **I** AM! I AM NOT EVEN **IMPORTANT** ENOUGH TO UNTIE THE STRAPS ON HIS **SANDALS!**

THE ONE WHO COMES **AFTER** ME IS **AHEAD** OF ME ALREADY... BECAUSE HE WAS **BEFORE** ME!

I AM BAPTIZING YOU WITH **WATER**... BUT **HE** WILL BAPTIZE YOU WITH **THE HOLY SPIRIT!**

....

WHAT SORT OF PERSON WILL MESSIAH **BE** IF HE IS EVEN **GREATER** THAN JOHN THE BAPTIZER ?!

SO LET US **PREPARE** OURSELVES FOR THE ONE WHO COMES LATER!

IF YOU HAVE **EXTRA** CLOTHES, YOU SHOULD **SHARE** WITH THOSE WHO HAVE **NONE!** IF YOU HAVE **EXTRA FOOD,** YOU SHOULD DO THE **SAME!**

Matthew 3:1-12 Mark 1:1-8 Luke 3:1-18 John 1:19-28 **51**

YOU *TAX COLLECTORS*... DON'T YOU *CHEAT* ANYONE BY COLLECTING *MORE* FROM THEM THAN IS *REQUIRED* BY THE ROMAN AUTHORITIES!

YOU *SOLDIERS*... DON'T FORCE PEOPLE TO GIVE YOU *MONEY* BY BRINGING *FALSE CHARGES* AGAINST THEM... BE *HAPPY* WITH THE PAY YOU *RECEIVE* FOR YOUR WORK!

*I*N THIS WAY JOHN THE BAPTIZER SAID MANY OTHER THINGS TO WARN THE PEOPLE EVERY DAY... AND HE PREACHED THE GOOD NEWS OF GOD'S COMING KINGDOM TO THEM... UNTIL ONE DAY...

Matthew 3:1-12 Mark 1:1-8 Luke 3:1-18 John 1:19-28

Matthew 3:13-17 Mark 1:9-11 Luke 3:21-22

4. PREPARATION FOR MINISTRY

HYOOO

OOO...

RIGHT AFTER YESHUAH WAS BAPTIZED BY JOHN, HE WENT OUT INTO THE DESERT WHERE NO GRASS GROWS...

THIS IS THE **GOOD NEWS**... THAT GOD OUR FATHER **LOVES** HIS PEOPLE! HE WANTS TO **FORGIVE** THEM AND SHOW THEM **THE WAY** TO BE SET FREE...

THAT IS WHY I HAVE BEEN SENT... TO REVEAL THIS TO THE PEOPLE FOR THE **REST OF MY LIFE!**

FOR THAT REASON I WILL **PREPARE** MYSELF... ...BY **PRAYING** ALONE TO MY FATHER GOD IN THIS **BARREN** PLACE!

ZHH

Matthew 4:1-11 Mark 1:12,13 Luke 4:1-13

IT IS WRITTEN: "WORSHIP THE LORD YOUR GOD... HE IS THE ONLY ONE YOU SHOULD SERVE!"

GET *AWAY* FROM ME, SATAN...

!!

VSSSHHH

HYUU UUU...

THEN SATAN LEFT YESHUAH ALONE...

HOWEVER, SATAN WAS NOT FINISHED...

... AND AFTERWARD, GOD SENT HIS HOLY ANGELS TO ENCIRCLE YESHUAH AND SERVE HIM...

... BUT HE KNEW HE HAD TO WAIT AND PLAN HIS NEXT ATTACK FOR A MORE FAVORABLE TIME!

@!≠#X!

Matthew 4:1-11   Mark 1:12,13   Luke 4:1-13   **59**

SOON AFTER...

SOME OF THE PEOPLE WHO WERE BAPTIZED BY JOHN CAME TO HIM, ASKING ABOUT THE SAVIOR KING WHO WAS SUPPOSED TO COME...

THESE WERE DISCIPLES OF JOHN THE BAPTIZER!

IS IT TRUE, JOHN...?

MESSIAH... THE ANOINTED KING PROMISED BY GOD... HAS APPEARED?

YES, ANDREW, IT'S TRUE!

I BAPTIZED HIM IN THE JORDAN OVER A MONTH AGO!

LOOK! THERE HE IS NOW...

...THE LAMB OF GOD WHO TAKES AWAY THE SIN OF THE WORLD!!

OH!

WHAT A HOLY MAN!!

HEY--
THAT'S
PHILIP
!!

HE'S
ALSO
FROM OUR
TOWN OF
BETHSAIDA
!!

R-RABBI!!
PHILIP
IS FROM
THE *SAME*
TOWN
AS US!

HE'S A
FISHERMAN
AND A
DISCIPLE
OF JOHN THE
BAPTIZER,
TOO!!

5. AT THE WEDDING IN CANA

RABBI, **WHY** YOU ARE IN SUCH A **HURRY**?

....

A FRIEND IS GETTING **MARRIED**!

... AND I TOLD MY **MOTHER** I'D BE THERE!

OH, YESHUAH !!!

YOU'VE ALL COME FOR THE **WEDDING**! HOW **WONDERFUL**!

THE MOTHER OF... RABBI!

MIRYAM (NOW IN HER MID-FORTIES)

WOW! CHECK OUT *THIS* WEDDING!

OH! DEAR... OH! DEAR...

WHOA, ANDREW.. TAKE IT *EASY!*

YEAH! THE FOOD IS *GREAT!*

UMMM ... YESHUAH... OUR *HOSTS* HAVE A BIT OF A *PROBLEM* HERE...

WHAT'S *HAPPENED*, MOTHER? EVERYTHING APPEARS TO BE GOING *WELL* FOR THEM...

ACTUALLY, THE *GUESTS* HAVE FINISHED OFF *ALL THE WINE!* THERE'S *NONE* LEFT! *

* THIS WOULD HAVE BEEN A MAJOR SOCIAL EMBARRASSMENT FOR THE BRIDEGROOM AND HIS FAMILY. IN ADDITION, THERE WAS A STRONG ELEMENT OF RECIPROCITY ABOUT WEDDINGS IN ANCIENT MIDDLE EASTERN CULTURE. POSSIBLY THIS FAMILY WOULD HAVE BEEN INVOLVED IN A FINANCIAL LIABILITY FOR FAILING TO PROVIDE ADEQUATELY FOR THEIR GUESTS, SINCE IT WAS EVEN POSSIBLE, IN CERTAIN CIRCUMSTANCES, TO TAKE LEGAL ACTION AGAINST ANY MAN WHO FAILED TO PROVIDE AN APPROPRIATE WEDDING GIFT.

DEAR WOMAN... WHAT IS THAT TO YOU AND ME ?

IT'S NOT MY TIME TO ACT YET!

...

AFTER THIS EVENT IN CANA, YESHUAH WENT TO CAPERNAUM WITH HIS MOTHER, BROTHERS, AND DISCIPLES...

THEY STAYED THERE FOR JUST A FEW DAYS... AND THEN...

6. GOING TO JERUSALEM

YESHUAH'S MOTHER AND BROTHERS RETURNED TO NAZARETH...

CAPERNAUM

CANA

NAZARETH

JERUSALEM

... WHILE YESHUAH AND HIS DISCIPLES TRAVELED ON TO THE SOUTH!

WE MUST GO TO **JERUSALEM**!!

RABBI, **WHY** ARE WE GOING THERE **NOW**?!

IS IT SO WE CAN ATTEND THE **PASSOVER** FEAST?

THAT'S RIGHT!

THEN, ONE NIGHT...

NICODEMUS,
A MEMBER OF THE JEWISH COUNCIL AND A SCHOLAR

RABBI
...

WE *KNOW* ... BY THE MIRACULOUS SIGNS YOU'RE DOING ... THAT YOU'RE A TEACHER SENT BY *GOD!*

THERE WAS A MAN NAMED NICODEMUS WHO CAME TO YESHUAH...

HE WAS A ZEALOUS PHARISEE ... AND HE WANTED YESHUAH TO TELL HIM HOW HE COULD ENTER GOD'S KINGDOM!

GOD *LOVED* THE WORLD *SO MUCH* THAT HE GAVE HIS *ONE AND ONLY SON!*

EVERYONE WHO BELIEVES IN HIM WILL *NOT* DIE ... BUT WILL HAVE *ETERNAL LIFE!!!*

*N*ICODEMUS HAD MIXED EMOTIONS... HE BELIEVED YESHUAH WAS MESSIAH, BUT HE ALSO KNEW HE COULD LOSE HIS POSITION AND PRESTIGE...

....

...IF HE ACTUALLY DECLARED YESHUAH WAS MESSIAH TO HIS FELLOW PHARISEES!

*L*ATER, WHEN PASSOVER WAS OVER, YESHUAH AND HIS DISCIPLES LEFT JERUSALEM...

THEY TRAVELED ON TO THE NEXT PLACE WHERE THEY COULD PREACH THE GOOD NEWS!

THE JACOB THIS WOMAN SPOKE ABOUT WAS AN ANCESTOR OF BOTH THE JEWS AND THE SAMARITANS!

HE WAS A VERY RESPECTED MAN AMONG THE SAMARITANS! THIS WELL WAS CALLED "THE WELL OF JACOB"!

INDEED
...

ALL WHO DRINK *THIS* WATER WILL BE *THIRSTY* AGAIN!

BUT *ANYONE* WHO DRINKS THE WATER *I* GIVE WILL *NEVER* BE THIRSTY!

...THE WATER *I* GIVE WILL BECOME A *SPRING* BUBBLING UP TO *EVERLASTING* LIFE!

SIR, GIVE *ME* THIS WATER ... THEN *I'LL* NEVER GET THIRSTY...

...AND I WON'T HAVE TO KEEP COMING HERE TO GET WATER!

GO! FETCH YOUR *HUSBAND* AND COME *BACK!*

GULP!

I -- I HAVE NO HUSBAND !!

YOU'RE *RIGHT* WHEN YOU SAY YOU DON'T HAVE A *HUSBAND!*

THE *FACT* IS, YOU'VE HAD *FIVE* HUSBANDS ... AND YOU AREN'T EVEN *MARRIED* TO THE MAN YOU LIVE WITH *NOW!* WHAT YOU HAVE JUST SAID IS *VERY TRUE!*

MANY SAMARITANS FROM SYCHAR BELIEVED IN YESHUAH BECAUSE OF THE WOMAN'S TESTIMONY, AND THEY BEGGED HIM TO STAY...

HE REMAINED TWO DAYS, AND HIS TEACHING LED MANY MORE TO BELIEVE HE REALLY WAS THE SAVIOR OF THE WORLD!

THEN THEY HEADED ON TO GALILEE...!

CAPERNAUM

CANA

SEA OF GALILEE

NAZARETH

SYCHAR

YAAAY!

YAAAY!

W-WOW! WHAT AN *EMOTIONAL* WELCOME!

I GUESS A *LOT* OF THESE PEOPLE WERE AT THE PASSOVER FEAST IN *JERUSALEM* AND *SAW* WHAT RABBI *DID* THERE!

THE DISCIPLES WERE BECOMING PROUD OF THEMSELVES...

BUT YESHUAH DIDN'T ACCEPT PRAISE FROM PEOPLE...

YESHUAH SPENT MORE TIME WITH GOD THE FATHER... AND HE WOULD ONLY ENTRUST HIMSELF TO GOD ALONE...

SO *THAT'S* WHY HE WAS *RUSHING* TO COME HERE...

BUT *KING HEROD ANTIPAS* IS THE ONE WHO PUT JOHN THE BAPTIZER IN *PRISON!*

WE *DON'T* WANT TO BE INVOLVED WITH *HIM!*

HOW WILL RABBI DEAL WITH *THIS?*

IT SEEMS YOU PEOPLE WILL *NEVER* BELIEVE...

...UNLESS YOU SEE MIRACULOUS SIGNS AND WONDERS!!

LORD, PLEASE COME DOWN TO OUR HOUSE BEFORE MY SON DIES!

THERE'S NO TIME FOR US TO LOSE!!

....

YOU MAY RETURN *WITHOUT* ME...

YOUR SON WILL *LIVE!!!*

I REQUEST HIM TO *COME*...AND HE COMMANDS ME TO *GO*...

IS... IS HE *TESTING* ME?

YES, HE WANTS ME TO *PROVE* I *BELIEVE* HE CAN DO THIS ... WITHOUT EVEN *SEEING* IT! B-BUT AT THIS *DISTANCE* ... ? ... I ... I MUST *TRUST* HIM!

THANK YOU VERY MUCH FOR YOUR *WORD!*

I'M GOING BACK HOME!

THE NEXT DAY...

M-MASTER!! I HAVE WONDERFUL NEWS!

MY SERVANTS !!

OH!!

WHEN DID HE GET BETTER ?!

Y-YOUR SON WAS HEALED !!!

POKKA-DA!

POKKA-DA!

THE FEVER LEFT HIM YESTERDAY AFTERNOON AT ONE O' CLOCK!

THAT WAS THE EXACT TIME YESHUAH HAD SAID TO THE ROYAL OFFICER, "YOUR SON WILL LIVE!"

WHEN HE TOLD THEM THIS, HIS WHOLE HOUSEHOLD BELIEVED IN YESHUAH!

NAZARETH

"THE SPIRIT OF THE LORD..."

"...IS ON ME!"

WE'RE IN HIS HOMETOWN, SO I'M SURE THEY'LL LISTEN TO HIM WELL!

...OR NOT!

RABBI'S READING THE SCROLL OF THE PROPHET ISAIAH!

WHISPER

WHISPER

Luke 5:1-11

Chapter **II**

MATTHEW

Matthew 9:9-13   Mark 2:13-17   Luke 5:27-32   **117**

YESHUAH SPOKE OF THESE THINGS IN PARABLES ("EARTHLY STORIES WITH HEAVENLY MEANINGS")...

HE USED PARABLES TO ILLUSTRATE TO THE PEOPLE HOW HIS TEACHING WAS DIFFERENT FROM THE OLD CUSTOMS OF THE PHARISEES...

THE SECOND PASSOVER AFTER YESHUAH BEGAN HIS MINISTRY WAS APPROACHING...

WOWWW... IT *ALWAYS* FILLS YOU WITH *AWE* TO ENTER THE GATES OF JERUSALEM, THE *HOLY CITY!*

THIS ONE IS THE *SHEEP GATE* ... IT LEADS TO THE *POOL OF BETHESDA* SURROUNDED BY COLUMNS!

LOOK AT ALL THESE *BLIND, LAME,* AND *PARALYZED* PEOPLE LYING BY THE *POOL* !!

BUT WH-WHY ...?!

PEOPLE BELIEVE THE *WATERS* OF THIS POOL CAN HEAL SICKNESS... *THAT'S* WHY SO MANY ARE HERE!

I FEEL SO SORRY FOR THEM!

"HERE IS MY SERVANT.
I TAKE GOOD CARE OF HIM.
I HAVE CHOSEN HIM AND AM
SO VERY PLEASED WITH HIM.
I HAVE PLACED MY OWN
SPIRIT UPON HIM.
HE'LL MAKE THINGS RIGHT
BETWEEN THE NATIONS.
HE WON'T CALL ATTENTION
TO HIMSELF BY SHOUTING IN
THE STREETS..."

AFTER THAT, YESHUAH WENT UP ON A MOUNTAIN TO BE ALONE...

...AND THERE HE SPENT ALL NIGHT PRAYING TO GOD!

THE NEXT MORNING...

I'M PICKING *TWELVE* OF YOU ... OUT OF MORE THAN 100 DISCIPLES... TO BE MY *SPECIAL* MESSENGERS ¦

...MY CHOSEN APOSTLES !!!

PETER!

ANDREW!

JUDAS ISCARIOT

THADDAEUS

SIMON
THE ZEALOT

PHILIP

THOMAS

JAMES, SON
OF ALPHAEUS

NATHANAEL
BARTHOLOMEW

MATTHEW

PETER

JAMES

ANDREW

JOHN

10. SERMON ON THE MOUNT

BLESSED ARE THOSE WHO RECOGNIZE THEIR SPIRITUAL NEED... FOR THE KINGDOM OF HEAVEN BELONGS TO THEM!

EIGHT BLESSINGS

BLESSED ARE THOSE WHO ARE SAD... FOR THEY WILL BE COMFORTED!

BLESSED ARE THOSE WHO ARE GENTLE AND HUMBLE HEARTED... FOR THEY WILL BE GIVEN THE EARTH!

BLESSED ARE THOSE WHO HUNGER AND THIRST FOR ALL THAT IS RIGHT... FOR THEY WILL BE FILLED!

BLESSED ARE THOSE WHO ARE MERCIFUL TOWARDS OTHERS... FOR THEY WILL BE SHOWN MERCY!

BLESSED ARE THOSE WHOSE HEARTS ARE PURE... FOR THEY WILL SEE GOD!

BLESSED ARE THOSE WHO PURSUE PEACE... FOR THEY WILL BE CALLED THE CHILDREN OF GOD!

BLESSED ARE THOSE WHO SUFFER FOR DOING WHAT IS RIGHT... FOR THE KINGDOM OF HEAVEN BELONGS TO THEM!

GOD AND RICHES

IT'S *NOT POSSIBLE* TO SERVE *BOTH* GOD AND MONEY! ONE OR THE OTHER WILL BE YOUR *MASTER!*

DON'T *WORRY* ABOUT WHAT YOU'LL *EAT... DRINK* ... OR WHAT YOU'LL *WEAR!*

YOUR FATHER IN HEAVEN *KNOWS EXACTLY* WHAT YOU NEED!

DON'T WORRY

DON'T *CONDEMN* OTHER PEOPLE!

YOU'LL BE JUDGED IN THE *SAME* WAY YOU JUDGE *OTHERS!*

DON'T CONDEMN OTHERS

SIMPLY *ASK...*

AND IT WILL BE *GIVEN* TO YOU!

FEW PEOPLE FIND THE *TRUE WAY* TO GOD!

THE GATE THAT LEADS TO *DEATH* IS *WIDE,* BUT THE GATE THAT LEADS TO *LIFE ITSELF* IS A NARROW ONE!

NARROW & WIDE GATES

BEWARE OF FALSE PROPHETS

EVERY *GOOD* TREE PRODUCES *GOOD FRUIT !!*

BUT A *BAD* TREE BEARS BAD FRUIT! SO YOU'LL *KNOW* THEM BY THEIR *FRUIT!*

ASK GOD

134   Matthew 6:24–7:20   Luke 16:13, 12:22-32, 6:37-45, 11:9-13, 13:22-24

NOT EVERYONE WHO *SAYS* THEY'RE MY DISCIPLE WILL ENTER GOD'S KINGDOM, BUT *ONLY* THOSE WHO ACTUALLY *DO* THE WILL OF MY FATHER!

AT THE *FINAL JUDGMENT* MANY WILL BOAST THAT THEY DID *GREAT THINGS* IN MY NAME, BUT I'LL TELL THEM, "GET AWAY FROM ME! I *NEVER* KNEW YOU!"

WHO WILL ENTER THE KINGDOM?

EVERYONE WHO HEARS MY WORDS, AND *OBEYS* THEM, IS LIKE ONE WHO BUILDS A HOUSE ON *SOLID ROCK!*

THE *WINDS* MAY BLOW AND THE *FLOODS* MAY COME, BUT A HOUSE ESTABLISHED ON *ROCK* WILL STAND!

A SOLID FOUNDATION

AFTER HE FINISHED SAYING ALL THESE THINGS, YESHUAH CAME DOWN FROM THE MOUNTAINSIDE... AND LARGE CROWDS FOLLOWED HIM!

HIS ENTHUSIASTIC PREACHING CAUSED YESHUAH'S POPULARITY TO GAIN MOMENTUM...

... AND HIS MANY MIRACULOUS WORKS CAUSED HIS NAME TO SPREAD RAPIDLY ACROSS THE LAND!

TWO SIGNIFICANT EVENTS OCCURRED DURING THIS TIME...

FIRST, HE HEALED THE SERVANT OF ANOTHER ROMAN COMMANDER IN CAPERNAUM...

AMAZING! I HAVEN'T COME ACROSS *THIS* KIND OF STRONG FAITH *ANYWHERE* IN ISRAEL!

GO NOW! IT WILL BE DONE *JUST* AS YOU ASKED!

LORD, I KNOW ALL ABOUT *GIVING* AND *TAKING* ORDERS...

SO I *KNOW* IF *YOU* COMMAND IT, MY *SERVANT* WILL BE HEALED!

THE OTHER WAS THAT HE BROUGHT A WIDOW'S ONLY SON BACK FROM THE DEAD IN THE VILLAGE OF NAIN...

THERE'S NO NEED TO *CRY* ANYMORE...

O...OH!

YOUNG MAN, I TELL YOU... *GET UP!*

MEANWHILE, JOHN THE BAPTIZER WAS STILL IMPRISONED BY KING HEROD ANTIPAS...

PRISON FORTRESS OF MACHAERUS, OVERLOOKING THE DEAD SEA

JOHN'S DISCIPLES BROUGHT HIM REGULAR REPORTS ON YESHUAH'S ACTIVITIES... AND THEY WEREN'T THE ACTIONS OF THE "CONQUERING KING" HE HAD EXPECTED! LOCKED AWAY FROM THE OPEN DESERT SPACES WHERE HE HAD ONCE PREACHED WITH CERTAINTY, DARK DOUBTS HAD BEGUN TO BREED IN THE DISMAL CONFINES OF HIS CELL...

. . . .

RABBI! JOHN THE BAPTIZER HAS **SENT** ME TO ASK YOU A **QUESTION**...

ARE YOU THE ONE WE'VE BEEN **WAITING** FOR? OR IS **ANOTHER** COMING?

SO JOHN SENT ONE OF HIS DISCIPLES TO YESHUAH...

. . .

GO **BACK** TO JOHN... **TELL** HIM WHAT YOU **SEE**! **TELL** HIM WHAT YOU **HEAR**!

BLESSED ARE THOSE WHO DO **NOT** LOSE **FAITH** BECAUSE OF ME!

JOHN'S FAITH IN YESHUAH WAVERED, BUT HIS STATURE AS A TREMENDOUS SERVANT OF GOD WAS NOT DIMINISHED!

AS JOHN'S DISCIPLE WAS LEAVING, YESHUAH BEGAN TO COMPLIMENT JOHN...

WHO DID YOU GO INTO THE DESERT TO SEE? A PROPHET? YES! AND HE IS MUCH MORE THAN A PROPHET! I TELL YOU **NO ONE GREATER** THAN JOHN THE BAPTIZER **HAS EVER BEEN BORN!**

Luke 7:36-50

BUT THE PHARISEES HARDENED THEIR HEARTS TOWARD YESHUAH'S WISDOM... AND SOUGHT TO DESTROY HIM!

THEY PLANNED TO DENY PUBLICLY THAT YESHUAH WAS MESSIAH!

IT'S *RABBI*!!

MARY MAGDALENE

THERE WERE OTHERS WHO LOVED AND SUPPORTED YESHUAH BESIDES HIS DISCIPLES, INCLUDING MANY WOMEN WHOSE LIVES HAD BEEN CHANGED FOREVER!

RABBI!!

WOW! SHE REALLY *IS* HEALED! TO THINK PEOPLE USED TO CALL HER THE "SEVEN-DEMON LADY"!!

ONE OF THESE WAS MARY MAGDALENE...

ANOTHER WAS SUSANNA, WHO WAS ALSO HEALED BY YESHUAH...

AND JOANNA, WHOSE HUSBAND CHUZA WAS THE MANAGER OF HEROD'S ENTIRE HOUSEHOLD...

Matthew 12:22-32 Mark 3:20-30 Luke 11:14-23

THE PERSON WHO DOES THE WILL OF MY *FATHER IN HEAVEN*...

THAT PERSON IS MY *BROTHER*... MY *SISTER*... MY *MOTHER!*

YESHUAH'S WORDS DID NOT EXPRESS HOSTILITY TOWARD HIS FAMILY...

BUT HIS TEACHING DEFINED A NEW FAMILY RELATIONSHIP... ONE CREATED BY MUTUAL FAITH... THE FAMILY OF GOD!

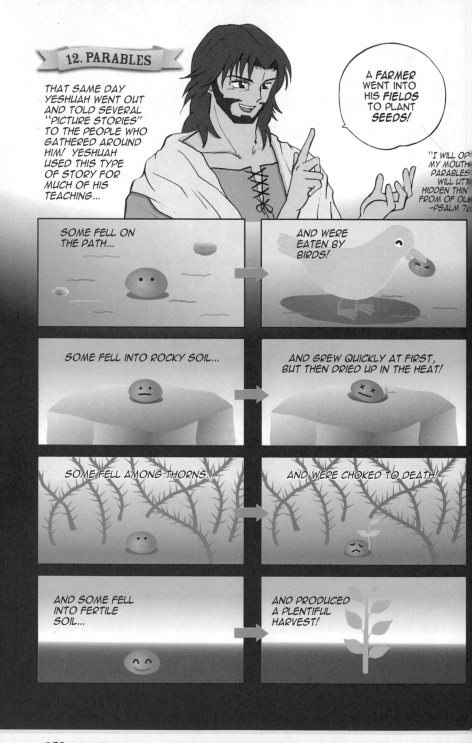

THE SEEDS MUST BE... *GOD'S WORD!*

AND THE *GOOD SOIL* MUST BE SOMEONE WHO *BELIEVES* THE WORD OF GOD!

I TELL YOU THE CROP WAS THIRTY, SIXTY, EVEN *ONE HUNDRED TIMES* WHAT WAS SOWN!

BUT, RABBI...

WHY DO YOU SPEAK TO THE PEOPLE IN THESE *"PICTURE STORIES"?*

THE *SECRETS* OF THE *KINGDOM* ARE BEING REVEALED TO *YOU*...

BUT *OTHER PEOPLE* ARE NOT YET *READY* FOR THEM!

THOSE WHO HAVE *MUCH* WILL BE GIVEN EVEN *MORE*...

AND THOSE WHO HAVE *LITTLE* ... WELL, EVEN WHAT LITTLE THEY *HAVE* WILL BE *TAKEN AWAY!*

IT'S A *TREMENDOUS* GIFT FROM GOD TO HAVE EYES THAT *SEE*, AND EARS THAT *HEAR!*

AND THERE WERE MORE PARABLES...

PARABLE OF THE MEASUREMENTS...

WITH THE MEASURE *YOU* USE, IT WILL BE MEASURED *TO YOU*....

YOU *DON'T KNOW* HOW A TINY *SEED* BURSTS FORTH TO BECOME A *PLANT*...

PARABLE OF THE GROWING SEED...

NEITHER DO YOU UNDERSTAND THE *KINGDOM* OF GOD!

PARABLE OF THE WEEDS...

THE KINGDOM OF GOD CAN *ALSO* BE COMPARED TO *THIS*...

A FARMER HAD GOOD SEED PLANTED IN HIS FIELD...

BUT WHILE HE SLEPT, AN ENEMY CAME...

AND PLANTED WEEDS AMONG THE WHEAT!

BOTH GOOD SEEDS AND BAD GREW TOGETHER... AND WHEN HARVEST CAME...

THE WEEDS WERE MIXED IN WITH THE GRAIN!

THE PARABLES OF...

THE MUSTARD SEED
AND THE YEAST...

THE TREASURE IN THE FIELD...

THE KINGDOM OF HEAVEN IS LIKE A *TINY* MUSTARD SEED, WHICH GROWS INTO A *LARGE* TREE WITH BIRDS RESTING IN ITS BRANCHES!

A MAN DISCOVERED *TREASURE* IN A FIELD...

HE *HID* IT AGAIN AND, WITH GREAT *JOY*, SOLD *EVERYTHING* HE OWNED AND *BOUGHT* THAT FIELD!

SIMILARLY, A LITTLE YEAST WORKS THROUGH *ALL* THE DOUGH!

THE PRICELESS PEARL...

THE KINGDOM OF HEAVEN IS LIKE A *TRADER* SEEKING *FINE* PEARLS...

THE KINGDOM OF HEAVEN IS LIKE A FISHING NET *LOADED* WITH FISH!

THE FISHER NETS...

CHUK
CHUK
CHUK

WHEN HE *FOUND* ONE THAT WAS *INCREDIBLY* VALUABLE, HE SOLD *EVERYTHING* HE HAD AND *BOUGHT* THAT PEARL!

ON SHORE, THE FISHERMAN *SORTS* THE FISH, GATHERING THE *GOOD* INTO BASKETS AND THROWING AWAY THE *BAD*!

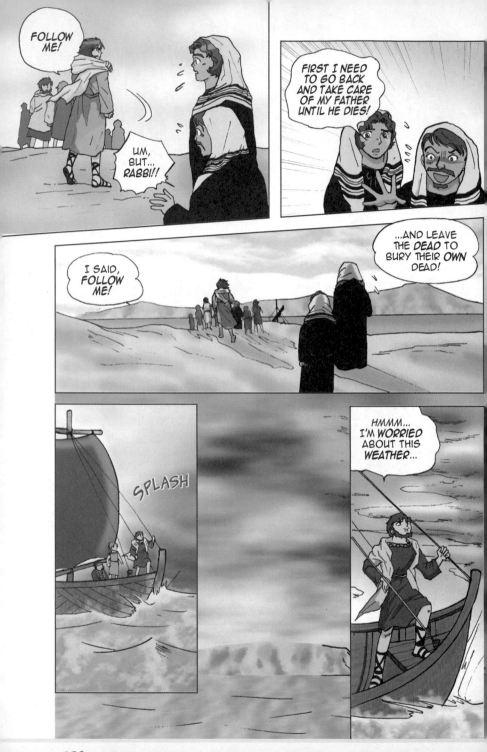

H-HUH? WHAT'S THE MATTER ?!!
TWITCH
UINK!! UINK!!
TWITCH
UINK!! UINK!!
UINK!!
TWITCH
SQUEEEE....
SPLASH!
SPLASH!
HEY... WAIT! STOP!!
RUMBLE
RUMBLE
!!?
LOOK!! LOOK AT THE TWO MEN!!
WHA-- WHAT HAPPENED?
WHAT AM I DOING HERE?

Matthew 9:36-38, 10:5-15   Mark 6:7-13   Luke 9:1-6

14. DEATH OF JOHN THE BAPTIZER

HEROD ANTIPAS, RULER OF GALILEE

GREAT BIRTHDAY PARTY, HERODIAS! WONDERFUL... THIS *GIRL* IS AMAZING!!

DOWN, BOY...

PARTY OR *NOT*, WE HAVE *BUSINESS* TO DISCUSS!

WHAT ARE YOU PLANNING TO DO ABOUT *JOHN THE BAPTIZER*?

WH... WHAA--!!?

WH-WHAT CAN I DO? I CAN'T SAY 'NO' IN FRONT OF ALL MY GUESTS...

HER REQUEST FOR JOHN'S HEAD HAD COME THROUGH HER MOTHER...

... AND *PLEASE* HAVE IT BROUGHT TO ME *NOW*... ON A *PLATTER*... MY DEAR STEPFATHER!

GRANTED! SOMEONE BRING US THE HEAD OF JOHN THE BAPTIZER!

SLASH!

THUS ENDED THE EARTHLY LIFE OF THE FORERUNNER, JOHN THE BAPTIZER...

HEROD FELT GUILTY ABOUT KILLING JOHN ... LATER HE BEGAN TO THINK YESHUAH MIGHT BE JOHN, RETURNED FROM THE DEAD!

172   Matthew 14:1-12   Mark 6:14-29

Matthew 14:13-21   Mark 6:30-44   **173**

174   Matthew 14:13-21   Mark 6:30-44

Matthew 14:22-36   Mark 6:45-56

YESHUAH AND HIS DISCIPLES PASSED THROUGH THE TOWN OF TYRE, WHERE A GENTILE WOMAN CALLED OUT TO HIM...

LORD! SON OF DAVID!!

HAVE MERCY ON ME, LORD! MY DAUGHTER IS CONTROLLED BY A DEMON!!

WHEN MY *OWN* CHILDREN ARE *HUNGRY*, IS IT *RIGHT* TO THROW THEIR *FOOD* TO THE DOGS!?

HUH?

BUT, LORD... EVEN BEGGING *DOGS* GET TO EAT THE *CRUMBS* THAT FALL FROM THEIR *MASTER'S TABLE!*

THAT'S A *GREAT REPLY...* AND IT SHOWS A *STRONG FAITH...!* YOUR DESIRE IS GRANTED!

THANK YOU!

WHEN THE WOMAN RETURNED HOME, SHE FOUND HER DAUGHTER LYING IN BED...

THE DEMON HAD GONE!

*T*RAVELING THROUGH THE GENTILE VILLAGES EAST OF THE LAKE OF GALILEE, YESHUAH PERFORMED ANOTHER SIGN WHEN HE MIRACULOUSLY FED FOUR THOUSAND MEN...

Matthew 15:21-28, 32-39 Mark 7:24-30, 8:1-10 **183**

Matthew 16:1-17:9 Mark 8:27-9:9

IF SOMEONE *CHEATS* YOU, *MISTREATS* YOU, OR SAYS SOMETHING *BAD* ABOUT YOU, *GO* TO THAT PERSON!

TELL THAT PERSON WHAT YOU THINK HE DID *WRONG!* IF HE *LISTENS*, YOU'VE WON HIM BACK!

BUT, RABBI... WHAT IF HE DOES IT *AGAIN* AND *AGAIN*? HOW *MANY* TIMES DO I HAVE TO KEEP *FORGIVING* HIM?

AS MANY AS *SEVEN* TIMES?

NO, PETER... NOT JUST *SEVEN* TIMES...

...BUT *SEVENTY TIMES SEVEN* TIMES! YOU *MUST* FORGIVE *OTHERS* IN THE SAME WAY *GOD* FORGIVES *YOU!*

AT THAT TIME, YESHUAH'S BROTHERS ARRIVED FROM NAZARETH...

THEY URGED YESHUAH TO REVEAL HIMSELF TO THE WORLD...

BUT HE KNEW HIS OWN BROTHERS DID NOT REALLY BELIEVE IN HIM AND WOULD NOT CONSENT.

YESHUAH TRAVELED TO THE SOUTH FROM CAPERNAUM TO ATTEND THE JEWISH 'FESTIVAL OF BOOTHS'...

JERUSALEM

THE *ONE* YOU ARE *NOW* ABLE TO *SEE*...

...THE *VERY ONE* YOU ARE *TALKING* TO... *IT IS HE!*

I AM THE GOOD SHEPHERD!

THE ONE WHO *LAYS DOWN HIS LIFE* FOR THE SHEEP!

NO ONE *TAKES MY LIFE FROM ME,* I LAY IT DOWN BY MY *OWN CHOICE!*

... TO *GIVE* LIFE... OR TO *TAKE IT AWAY!*

THAT'S WHY THE *FATHER* HAS GIVEN ME *TREMENDOUS* AUTHORITY...

THOUGH THEY ARGUED AND DEBATED, THE PHARISEES AND PRIESTS COULDN'T COME TO ANY UNIFIED CONCLUSION REGARDING THE PERSON OF YESHUAH...

THAT MAN IS *POSSESSED* BY A *DEMON!!*

HE'S *RAVING MAD!!*

BUT CAN A DEMON MAKE A BLIND MAN SEE?

A FEW DAYS LATER, YESHUAH AND HIS DISCIPLES LEFT JERUSALEM.

THE SAMARITAN TOOK THE MAN TO AN INN... AND PAID ENOUGH FOR HIM TO STAY UNTIL HE HAD RECOVERED!

NOW WHICH OF THE THREE TRAVELERS WAS A NEIGHBOR TO THE INJURED MAN?

TH-THE SAM... URRR... THE ONE WHO TOOK PITY ON HIM...!

UGH! I CAN'T EVEN SAY THE "S" WORD!

THAT IS CORRECT! BUT WHAT YOU KNOW IS NOT NEARLY SO IMPORTANT AS HOW YOU LIVE....

SO, GO... AND DO THE SAME THING!

VILLAGE OF BETHANY

I CAN SEE THE HOUSE! COME ON!

WE'RE FINALLY HERE! I CAN'T WAIT TO SEE OUR GOOD FRIENDS LAZARUS, MARTHA, AND MARY!

I'M READY TO EAT!!

MARTHA

YESHUAH! WELCOME TO OUR HOME!!

RABBI! I'M PREPARING DINNER FOR ALL OF YOU!

HUH!

MARY

HI, YESHUAH !!

LAZARUS

HAHAHA

HAHAHA

HEY!

HAHAHA

WHEN THE STORY WAS FINISHED, PEOPLE LEFT MARVELING AND AMAZED AT THE POWER OF ITS MEANING!

I THINK THE *FATHER* IN THE STORY IS SUPPOSED TO BE *GOD*!

YEAH! ME, TOO!

AND IT'S LIKE... IF WE'RE *WILLING* TO TURN BACK TO HIM, HE'LL *FORGIVE* US... EVEN FOR THE *WORST* THINGS WE'VE DONE!

RABBI!

TUP TUP

15. LAZARUS DIES

HUH?

WHO'S THAT?!

RABBI!! IT'S LAZARUS!!

LAZARUS IS VERY SICK! HE MIGHT DIE!!

HUF HUF

PLEASE GO TO HIM... QUICKLY!!

OKAY... I'LL GO!

WHAT?! BACK TO JUDEA?!

HUF HUF

NO, RABBI!! IT'S TOO *DANGEROUS!* TH–THEY TRIED TO STONE US THERE JUST THE OTHER DAY!!

LISTEN TO ME... MY FRIEND LAZARUS... IS ALREADY *DEAD!*

BUT THIS HAS *HAPPENED* SO THAT YOU'LL *BELIEVE!* LET'S GO!

Chapter III

16. THE ENTRY TO JERUSALEM

TIME HAS PASSED SO *QUICKLY*... THIS WILL BE MY *FOURTH PASSOVER* WITH RABBI SINCE I BECAME HIS DISCIPLE....

SOMETIME LATER *YESHUAH* AND HIS DISCIPLES WERE HEADED TOWARD *JERUSALEM* AGAIN...

BE *PREPARED* FOR WHAT WILL *HAPPEN* IN JERUSALEM!

THE CHIEF PRIESTS AND TEACHERS OF THE LAW WILL SENTENCE ME TO *DEATH!*

I'LL BE *BEATEN* AND *ABUSED* BY GODLESS PEOPLE... AND MADE TO *SUFFER TERRIBLY!*

AND... IN THE END...*HUNG* ON A *CROSS!*

BUT... THREE DAYS LATER... I WILL BE *RAISED* FROM THE *DEAD!*

. . . .

IS THIS *PROPHECY?*

HE'S TOLD US THIS *TWICE* BEFORE... BUT *HOW* COULD IT HAPPEN IN *JERUSALEM?*

SEVERAL GREEK MEN WERE IN JERUSALEM FOR THE PASSOVER FEAST. THEY APPROACHED PHILIP WITH A REQUEST...

SIR, WE *AREN'T JEWS*, BUT WE ARE *BELIEVERS* WHO FEAR THE GOD OF ISRAEL!

WE *REALLY* WANT TO *MEET* YESHUAH!

PHILIP WENT TO ANDREW TO DISCUSS THIS, AND THEN TOGETHER THEY WENT TO SPEAK WITH YESHUAH ABOUT IT...

RABBI, *WHAT* DO YOU *THINK*?

....

UNLESS A GRAIN OF *WHEAT* IS BURIED IN THE *TOMB* OF THE EARTH...

...IT *REMAINS* MERELY ONE *SEED*!

BUT WHEN IT'S *BURIED*, IT *GROWS*...

...AND PRODUCES *MANY MORE SEEDS*!

NOW MY HEART IS *TROUBLED*!

OH, FATHER, SHOW THEM HOW GLORIOUS YOUR NAME IS!

THEN THERE WAS A VOICE FROM HEAVEN...

I HAVE GLORIFIED MY NAME... AND I WILL GLORIFY IT AGAIN!!

WHAT WAS THAT!?

THUNDER! I THINK...

NO! AN ANGEL... AND IT SPOKE TO THAT MAN!

THAT *VOICE* WAS FOR *YOUR* BENEFIT... NOT *MINE!*

NOW IS THE TIME FOR *MEN* TO BE *JUDGED...* AND FOR *THE PRINCE OF THIS WORLD* TO BE DRIVEN *OUT!*

BUT WHEN I'M *LIFTED UP...* I'LL GATHER *EVERYONE* TO MYSELF!

*T*HOSE GREEKS NEVER DID GET TO MEET YESHUAH THAT DAY....

BUT THEY HEARD THE VOICE FROM HEAVEN... AND YESHUAH'S WORDS THAT HE WOULD BRING TOGETHER BOTH JEWS AND BELIEVERS LIKE THEMSELVES FROM OUTSIDE OF ISRAEL...

AND THEY WERE SATISIFIED!

...THEY RETURNED TO THEIR OWN COUNTRY AND BECAME THE FORERUNNERS OF FAITH TO A MULTITUDE OF NON-JEWISH BELIEVERS!

THIS DAY WOULD BE LONG AND DIFFICULT... TEMPLE OFFICIALS AND RELIGIOUS ELDERS SOUGHT EVERY OPPORTUNITY TO TEST YESHUAH, CHALLENGING HIM WITH DIFFICULT QUESTIONS.

AHHH... WELL, *HERE'S* "MR. POPULAR" NOW!

I HAVE A *QUESTION* FOR YOU, YESHUAH OF NAZARETH!

BY WHAT *AUTHORITY* DID YOU DRIVE OUT THE *TEMPLE MERCHANTS* THE OTHER DAY!?

PRIESTS AND ELDERS OF JERUSALEM

.....

AND LET ME ASK *YOU*...

JOHN THE BAPTIST

WHERE DID JOHN THE BAPTIZER RECEIVE *HIS* AUTHORITY FROM?

HMMM...

UHH...

ERRGH.... IF I SAY *"FROM HEAVEN"* HE'LL ASK *WHY* WE DIDN'T *BELIEVE* JOHN! BUT IF I SAY *"FROM MAN"*...

...I'M AFRAID THE *CROWD* MAY TURN *AGAINST* US... SINCE THEY LOVED JOHN....

WE... UM... WE *DON'T* KNOW!

I SEE... WELL THEN I WON'T ANSWER *YOUR* QUESTION *EITHER!*

Matthew 21:33-45   Mark 12:1-12   Luke 20:9-19

NEXT THE PHARISEES CHALLENGED YESHUAH...

PHARISEES AND TEACHERS OF THE LAW

OH, YESHUAH! WE'D LIKE TO ASK YOU SOMETHING, *TOO*...

IS IT *RIGHT* FOR US TO PAY *TAXES* TO *CAESAR*, THE EMPEROR?!

AH *HA!* YOU *CAN'T* ANSWER *THAT* QUESTION *CAN* YOU?!

SAY "YES" AND YOU PROCLAIM CAESAR *KING OF ISRAEL* AND DENY YOUR GOD! *BUT* SAY "NO" AND...

...AH, WELL, *THAT'S TREASON*... AND YOU GET YOURSELF *ARRESTED!*

SO... *GO AHEAD*, YESHUAH... *ANSWER* THE QUESTION!

....

YOU *PHONIES!* WHY ARE YOU TRYING TO *TRAP* ME? *SHOW* ME A COIN USED FOR THE *TAX!*

WHOSE *PICTURE* IS ON THIS COIN? WHOSE *NAME?*

UM... CAESAR'S...

THEN *GIVE* TO CAESAR WHAT *BELONGS* TO CAESAR...

AND GIVE TO GOD WHAT *BELONGS* TO GOD!

Matthew 22:15-22   Mark 12:13-17   Luke 20:20-26   **225**

DHOOOOOUUUM!

SEE, RABBI, WE DON'T **BELIEVE** IN THE RESURRECTION OF THE **DEAD**, OKAY?

BUT **IF** IT WERE **TRUE**, OKAY, HOW WOULD YOU RESOLVE **THIS** PROBLEM?

THE THIRD GROUP TO APPROACH YESHUAH WAS THE SADDUCEES...

"THERE'S THIS **LADY** WHO MARRIES INTO A FAMILY OF **SEVEN BROTHERS**, SEE? HER HUSBAND **DIES**, BUT THEY DON'T HAVE CHILDREN, OKAY? SO SHE'S REQUIRED BY **LAW** TO MARRY HER **BROTHER-IN-LAW** TO CARRY ON HER HUSBAND'S NAME, RIGHT? RIGHT! OKAY, BUT THEN **HE** DIES, **TOO**, OKAY? SO SHE MARRIES THE **NEXT** BROTHER, WHO **ALSO** DIES CHILDLESS, AND SO ON... YADDA, YADDA... UNTIL **ALL SEVEN** DIE, AND SHE'S A **WIDOW** SEVEN TIMES OVER!!

NOW... AT THE RESURRECTION... **WHOSE** WIFE IS SHE GOING TO BE, OKAY?"

YOU **DON'T** UNDERSTAND THE **WORD OF GOD** BECAUSE YOU **DON'T** HAVE HIS **POWER** AND **WISDOM** LIVING IN YOU!

WHEN THE DEAD RISE, THEY **WON'T** MARRY OR BE GIVEN IN MARRIAGE BY THEIR PARENTS... THEY'LL BE LIKE THE ANGELS IN HEAVEN!

IN THE **ANCIENT TEXTS** IT IS WRITTEN: "I AM THE GOD OF ABRAHAM, THE GOD OF ISAAC, AND THE GOD OF JACOB...."

HE IS **NOT** THE GOD OF THE **DEAD**... BUT OF THE **LIVING**!!

THE SADDUCEES RETREATED IN SILENCE!

THE QUESTIONS KEPT ON COMING...

"WHAT IS THE MOST IMPORTANT COMMANDMENT IN THE LAW OF MOSES?"

THE TEACHERS OF THE LAW

"LOVE THE LORD YOUR GOD WITH ALL YOUR HEART... ALL YOUR SOUL... AND ALL YOUR MIND!"

THIS IS THE FIRST AND GREATEST LAW!

THE SECOND IS "LOVE YOUR NEIGHBOR THE SAME WAY YOU LOVE YOURSELF"!

"IS MESSIAH THE SON OF DAVID?"

THE PHARISEES

YOU SAY THAT MESSIAH WILL BE THE SON OF THE ANCIENT KING DAVID... BUT IN THE OLD WRITINGS DAVID HIMSELF CALLED MESSIAH HIS LORD! HOW CAN HE BE HIS SON?

THE PRETENSE AND DECEPTION OF THESE RELIGIOUS LEADERS ANGERED YESHUAH...

HE WARNED THE PEOPLE NOT TO ACT LIKE THEM, BECAUSE THEY DIDN'T PRACTICE WHAT THEY PREACHED...

THEN HE CRIED OUT:

OH, JERUSALEM... WHY DO YOU ALWAYS ATTACK AND KILL GOD'S MESSENGERS? NOW YOU WON'T SEE ME AGAIN UNTIL YOU SAY, "BLESSED IS HE WHO COMES IN THE NAME OF THE LORD!"

BUT YESHUAH DID ANSWER EVERY ONE OF THEIR QUESTIONS AND WON EVERY ARGUMENT WITH THEM...

UNTIL, FINALLY, THEY DIDN'T DARE ASK HIM ANY MORE QUESTIONS!

IT'S TWO DAYS BEFORE PASSOVER, WHEN I WILL BE HUNG ON A CROSS AND SACRIFICED...

FOR I AM THE LAMB OF GOD!

THIS WAS THE FOURTH TIME YESHUAH TOLD HIS DISCIPLES OF HIS COMING EXECUTION... AND THE LONG, HARD DAY FINALLY CAME TO AN END...

18. JUDAS THE BETRAYER

AFTER YESHUAH AND HIS DISCIPLES RETURNED TO BETHANY, THEY HAD A MEAL AT THE HOME OF MARTHA, MARY, AND LAZARUS...

WEDNESDAY, THE 13TH DAY IN THE MONTH OF NISAN

THEN...

MARY! IS THAT NARD PERFUME?! BE CAREFUL!!

SHE ALREADY BROKE IT OPEN!

OOH... SMELLS NICE...!

....

WSSH

WSSH

WHAT A WASTE! THAT PERFUME WAS WORTH MORE THAN A YEAR'S PAY!!

JUDAS?

WE COULD'VE SOLD IT AND GIVEN THE CASH TO THE POOR!

!

IN REALITY, JUDAS WAS NOT ESPECIALLY INTERESTED IN POOR PEOPLE...

HE WAS IN CHARGE OF THE GROUP'S FUNDS... AND OFTEN STOLE THEIR MONEY!

Matthew 26:6-16   Mark 14:3-11   **229**

Matthew 26:17-20   Mark 14:12-17   Luke 22:7-14   **231**

19. THE LORD'S SUPPER

Matthew 26:26-35   Mark 14:22-31   Luke 22:15-20, 22:31-34   John 13:36-38

20. GARDEN OF GETHSEMANE

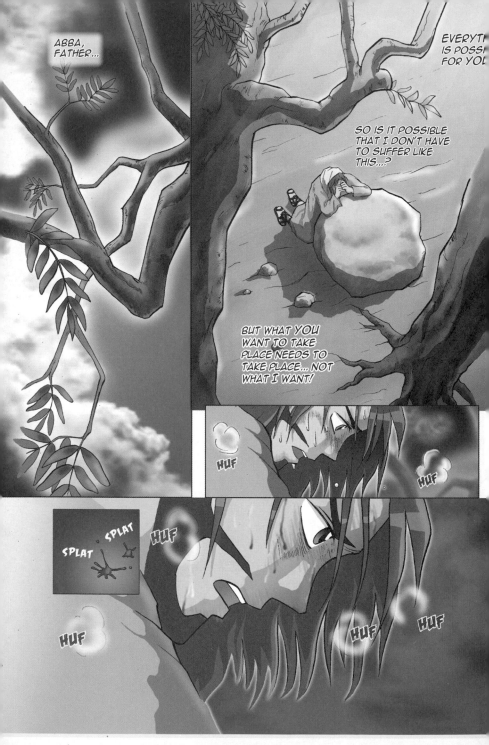

Matthew 26:36-46 Mark 14:32-42 Luke 22:40-46

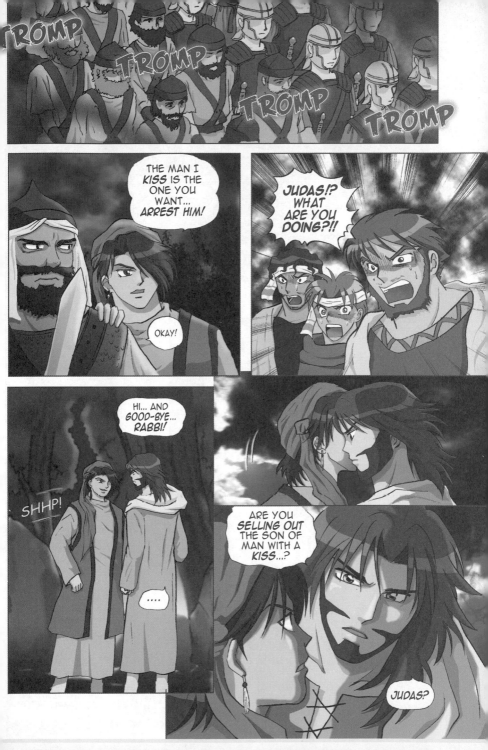

Matthew 26:47-56   Mark 14:43-50   Luke 22:47-53   John 18:2-11

21. THE WAY TO THE CROSS

YOU SAID YOU COULD *DESTROY* THIS TEMPLE AND *REBUILD* IT IN *THREE DAYS*... *DIDN'T YOU?*

I'VE SPOKEN *OPENLY* IN PUBLIC AND IN THE TEMPLE... *NOTHING* WAS SAID IN *SECRET*...

SO WHY QUESTION *ME?* ASK THOSE WHO *LISTENED* TO MY TEACHING!

SLAP!

HOW DARE YOU SPEAK TO ANNAS, THE HIGH PRIEST, LIKE THAT?!

CAIAPHAS, THE CHIEF PRIEST

AREN'T YOU GOING TO *ANSWER?!*

I *COMMAND* YOU TO TESTIFY... ARE YOU *MESSIAH?* SON OF THE *LIVING GOD?!*

IT'S NO USE TALKING TO HIM!

TAKE HIM TO CAIAPHAS, THE CHIEF PRIEST!!

MEANWHILE, JUDAS ISCARIOT WAS TORMENTED BY A GUILTY CONSCIENCE AND HURRIED BACK TO THE ELDERS...

HERE! T-TAKE BACK YOUR MONEY! I'VE BETRAYED AN INNOCENT MAN!!

G-GOD WILL NEVER FORGIVE M-ME!

TREMBLE

TREMBLE

SO WHAT?! WHY SHOULD WE CARE?

THAT'S YOUR PROBLEM!! GET OUT OF HERE... JUDAS!!

AT DAWN, JUDAS HANGED HIMSELF...

THAT SAME MORNING, AT THE PALACE OF PONTIUS PILATE, THE ROMAN GOVERNOR...

...HIS "BLODD MONEY" SCATTERED ACROSS THE TEMPLE FLOOR!

AT THAT TIME, ONLY THE ROMAN GOVERNMENT HAD THE LEGAL AUTHORITY TO EXECUTE CRIMINALS...

MY LORD, THE *JEWS* ARE REQUESTING THAT YOU *JUDGE* A MAN NAMED *YESHUAH*...

THEY'RE PRETTY *UPSET* AND CLAIM HE DESERVES TO *DIE!*

SO I HEARD...! BRING HIM IN!

SO THE JEWISH LEADERS BROUGHT THEIR CASE BEFORE PILATE, SEEKING TO HAVE YESHUAH PUT TO DEATH!

STOMP STOMP

PILATE'S CONDUCTING THE TRIAL... WILL HE *WORK* WITH US ON THIS ...OR *NOT?*

OKAY...WHAT *CHARGES* DO YOU HAVE *AGAINST* THIS MAN?

WELL, SIR... IF HE *WEREN'T* A *CRIMINAL* WE *WOULDN'T* BE HANDING HIM *OVER* TO YOU!

Matthew 27:11-31 Mark 15:1-20 Luke 23:1-25 John 18:28-19:16

22. CRUCIFIXION

KILL YESHUAH!!

KILL YESHUAH!!

A NEW TRIAL WAS CONVENED BEFORE PONTIUS PILATE SO HE COULD CONSIDER THE CHARGE THAT YESHUAH WAS A POLITICAL REBEL WHO OPPOSED THE ROMAN EMPEROR CAESAR...

... AND NOW THE PRIESTS HAD STIRRED UP A HOSTILE MOB TO JOIN THEM! THESE PEOPLE KEPT SHOUTING FOR YESHUAH TO BE KILLED!

LISTEN! I'VE FOUND NO REASON TO HAVE THIS MAN PUT TO DEATH!!

I'LL HAVE HIM WHIPPED, AND LET GO!!

SSRAKK!!

AHHH HHH!

Matthew 27:32-54 Mark 15:21-41 Luke 23:26-49 John 19:17-37

Matthew 27:32-54   Mark 15:21-41   Luke 23:26-49   John 19:17-37

HYOOOOOOOOO....

MY GOD...! MY GOD!!!

WHY HAVE YOU ABANDONED ME?!

AT THAT MOMENT, THE CURTAIN THAT HID THE HOLIEST OF ALL ROOMS IN THE TEMPLE WAS TORN IN TWO ... FROM TOP TO BOTTOM!

KRAAK!!

SHAA

SHAA

...

...

TH- THIS MAN **MUST** HAVE BEEN THE **SON OF GOD**!!!

SAAAAAHHH

IS HE REALLY **DEAD?**

YES!

ONE OF THE JEWISH COUNCIL, WHO WAS ALSO A FOLLOWER OF YESHUAH, ASKED PILATE IF HE COULD TAKE THE BODY FOR BURIAL, AND PILATE AGREED.

YESHUAH'S BODY WAS WRAPPED IN A CLEAN CLOTH OF LINEN...

AND LAID IN A TOMB CUT FROM SOLID ROCK...

SIR, THAT CRIMINAL SAID HE'D **RISE UP** FROM THE **DEAD** AFTER THREE DAYS...

WE'RE AFRAID HIS **DISCIPLES** WILL **STEAL** HIS BODY... AND **SAY** HE DID!!

SO... **SECURE** THE TOMB WITH **GUARDS** THEN...! **WHATEVER!!**

268 Matthew 27:32-54, 27:62-28:10 Mark 15:21-41, 16:1-11
Luke 23:26-49, 24:1-12 John 19:17-37, 20:1-18

Matthew 27:62-28:10   Mark 16:1-11   Luke 24:1-12   John 20:1-18

Matthew 27:62-28:10   Mark 16:1-11, 16:12-13
Luke 24:1-12, 24:13-35   John 20:1-18, 20:24-29

John 21:1-19

AFTER I LEAVE...

YOU MUST CONTINUE TO FOLLOW ME... AND FEED MY SHEEP!

PETER, THE ROCK... I HAVE A JOB FOR YOU!

THEN PETER KNEW THAT YESHUAH HAD FORGIVEN HIM COMPLETELY... AND THAT HE WOULD CONTINUE HIS WORK AS A DISCIPLE!

NEVER AGAIN WOULD HE RETURN TO HIS FISHING NETS...!

THE LAKE OF GALILEE, IN THE GARDEN WHERE PETER RECEIVED HIS CALL

DURING THE FORTY DAYS AFTER HIS RESURRECTION, YESHUAH APPEARED TO HIS DISCIPLES SEVERAL TIMES AND SPOKE TO THEM ABOUT GOD'S KINGDOM... AND THEN, BEFORE THEIR EYES, HE WAS TAKEN UP INTO HEAVEN.

GOD HIMSELF WILL DECIDE THE DAY OF MY RETURN...WHEN THE KINGDOM WILL COME ON EARTH...

FOR NOW I AM RETURNING TO THE FATHER... AND YOU WILL NOT SEE ME!

...BUT YOU WILL BE MY WITNESSES !!!

YES, LORD!!

MANY OTHER STORIES OF THE MIRACULOUS THINGS YESHUAH DID COULD BE INCLUDED HERE, BUT HOW COULD ANY ONE BOOK HOLD IT ALL?

IT IS UP TO YOU NOW...
THESE THINGS HAVE BEEN WRITTEN FOR YOU SO THAT YOU WILL BELIEVE YESHUAH IS MESSIAH, THE SON OF GOD, AND IF YOU BELIEVE IN HIM, YOU WILL HAVE THE ETERNAL LIFE THAT HE PROMISED.

IF YOU BELIEVE YESHUAH IS MESSIAH, YOU TOO CAN BECOME ONE OF HIS DISCIPLES. HE IS ALIVE, AND YOU CAN WALK WITH HIM AND TALK TO HIM JUST LIKE HIS DISCIPLES DID. TALKING TO YESHUAH IS CALLED PRAYER, AND YOU CAN PRAY USING EITHER HIS HEBREW NAME, YESHUAH, OR THE ENGLISH TRANSLATION OF HIS NAME, JESUS.

YESHUAH,
I BELIEVE YOU ARE THE SON OF GOD.
I WANT THE ETERNAL LIFE YOU PROMISED.
I REALIZE THAT I NEED YOU.
MY LIFE HAS NOT BEEN THE KIND OF LIFE THAT PLEASES GOD.
YOU KNOW THE THINGS I HAVE DONE; YOU SEE INTO MY HEART.
FORGIVE ME.

YESHUAH,
I WANT YOU TO COME INTO MY LIFE.
HELP ME TO FOLLOW YOU AND TO BE YOUR DISCIPLE.
GIVE ME CONFIDENCE TO FOLLOW YOU.
HELP ME TO LIVE AS YOU LIVED.
YESHUAH, I GIVE MY LIFE TO YOU.

THANK YOU FOR HEARING ME.
THANK YOU FOR CARING FOR ME.

YESHUAH, YOU ARE MY LORD AND MY SAVIOR.

AFTER TALKING WITH YESHUAH, PLEASE DO THESE THREE THINGS:
1. TELL THE PERSON WHO GAVE YOU THIS BOOK THAT YOU HAVE DECIDED TO FOLLOW YESHUAH.
2. READ THE ANCIENT TEXT, THE BIBLE, FOR YOURSELF.
3. FOLLOWERS OF YESHUAH GATHER FOR FELLOWSHIP. FIND AND JOIN A GATHERING OR CHURCH.

TO ALL WHO BELIEVED HIM AND ACCEPTED HIM, HE GAVE THE RIGHT TO BECOME CHILDREN OF GOD. THEY ARE REBORN—NOT WITH A PHYSICAL BIRTH RESULTING FROM HUMAN PASSION OR PLAN, BUT A BIRTH THAT COMES FROM GOD. (JOHN 1:12-13)

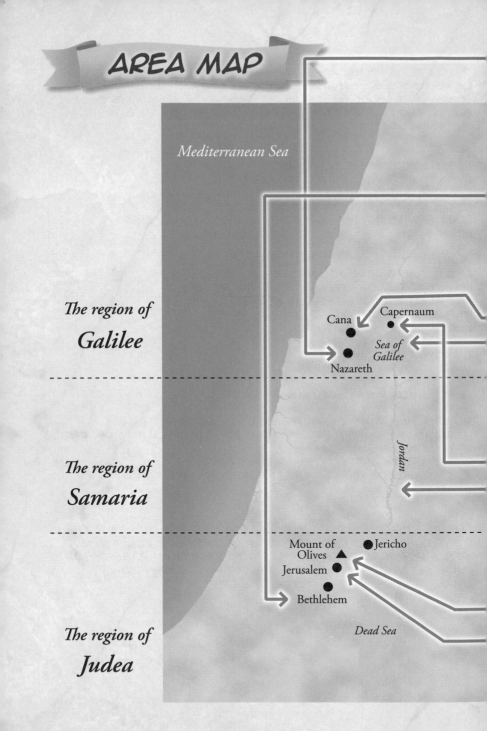

AREA MAP

Mediterranean Sea

The region of
Galilee

Cana

Capernaum

Sea of Galilee

Nazareth

The region of
Samaria

Jordan

The region of
Judea

Mount of Olives

Jericho

Jerusalem

Bethlehem

Dead Sea

NAZARETH

A village in northern Galilee, where Miryam and Yosef live. This is where Miryam saw the angel who told her that she would become the mother of Yeshuah!

BETHLEHEM

A town in Judea, known as "the City of the Great King." Yeshuah is born there when Yosef and Miryam are visiting as part of a population study.

CANA

A town in Galilee to the north of Nazareth. Yeshuah presents a groom and bride with an amazing wedding gift in this place!

SEA OF GALILEE

A large freshwater lake through which the Jordan River flows from north to south ... and the site of miracles that defy any human logic!

The hometown of Peter and Andrew, which Yeshuah uses as a base of operations.

CAPERNAUM

JORDAN

The place where John the Baptizer immerses people in water as a "rite of passage." Even Yeshuah asks John to immerse him, too.

MOUNT OF OLIVES

Yeshuah spends a lot of time at the foot of this mountain ridge, in the Garden of Gethsemane.

JERUSALEM

"The City of Peace," a sacred town in Judea where the "Feast of Passover" is celebrated every spring. This is the place where Messiah will face terrible trials ... and experience the greatest triumph in the history of the world!

283

CHARACTER PROFILES

Messiah Yeshuah

Anyone who meets him can tell in seconds that Yeshuah's not like any man ever seen before in this world ... But is he really Messiah, the liberating God-King that everyone's been waiting for? How could Messiah possibly be a working man from a backward town like Nazareth?

Yosef & Miryam

This decent, young couple descended from the greatest king in history and are Yeshuah's parents ... or at least Miryam is his mother. Questions have circulated for years about who his father really is!

Zechariah & Elizabeth

Miryam's relative Elizabeth is married to a temple priest. In their old age they had a baby, and although Zechariah didn't talk about it much at first, he now insists an angel told him his son would be...

John the Baptizer

John is a "Nazirite" – a person who takes a holy vow to never cut his hair or drink wine. His warnings to the people to clean up their lives prepare the way for Yeshuah but get him in trouble with Herod Antipas.

The Two Herods

King Herod the Great governs Judea at the time of Yeshuah's birth. His insecurity about being replaced by Messiah leads him to commit a hideous massacre. His son, Herod Antipas, is responsible for horrible crimes as well.

Herodias

Herodias is the wife of Herod Antipas. She hates John the Baptizer because he has denounced her perverse marriage. She uses her beautiful daughter to gain revenge!

Nicodemus

A member of the ruling council who believes Yeshuah really is Messiah ... but who is too frightened to share that opinion with anyone else, especially after Yeshuah tells him what it will really take to enter the Kingdom!

Pharisees & Scribes

These men are interpreters and teachers of the ancient texts and are well-known for their strict observance of tradition. They constantly oppose Yeshuah, because they think he is intent on breaking those very laws and customs. However, they are frustrated that they seem to find themselves on the losing side of every debate!

Zacchaeus

Zacchaeus is a tax collector in Jericho. His authority to collect taxes for the Empire – including whatever "extra" he can skim off the top for himself – has made him very wealthy. He is disliked for his profession and disrespected because he's very, very short.

the Women

These volunteers and supporters from Galilee help Yeshuah and his followers financially and practically. Mary of Magdala is one of these women. Others in the group include Joanna, the wife of Chuza, who manages King Herod's household, and Susanna.

Martha, Mary, and Lazarus

Lazarus is one of Yeshuah's best friends, and Martha and Mary are his sisters. They all live in Bethany, and when Yeshuah travels to Jerusalem he usually stays at their house. When there is a serious illness in the family, they call for Yeshuah and are devastated when he doesn't arrive in time!

Pontius Pilate

Pontius Pilate is the Empire's "prefect" or lower military governor for the areas of Judea, Samaria, and Idumaea. He is widely known for his arrogance and serious lack of empathy for other cultures and their differences, but he is receptive to the advice of his wife.

THE TWELVE

These are the handpicked
followers of Yeshuah who are
given power to heal sicknesses,
bring the dead back to life, and
overcome demonic forces!

Peter (Simon) & Andrew

These brothers live as fishermen on
Lake Galilee and are the first to become
followers. Andrew, the younger brother,
has also followed John the Baptizer.
When Andrew first introduces Simon
to Yeshuah, Simon gets a new name...
Peter ("the Rock"). But will this Rock
crumble when the going gets tough?

Judas Iscariot

Judas is the disciple in charge of the group's finances. Beyond that, little is certain about him. Does his second name indicate he's one of the Sicarii, the "knife man" sect of the Zealots who seek to overthrow the Empire ... or merely that he's from the small Judean town of Kerioth? Nobody seems to be sure, and the thoughts of this quiet but intense disciple are known only to himself ... and Yeshuah!

Philip

This disciple has an obsession with numbers... but has he counted the cost of following a controversial Messiah?

Nathanael Bartholomew

Philip's close friend Nathanael is a devout scholar ... one whose book knowledge could cause him to miss the big picture!

Matthew

Only Yeshuah would dare make a hated tax collector part of his group ... and he even knows Matthew will one day write a "tell all" book about him!

Thomas the Twin   Thaddaeus (Jude)   Simon the Zealot   James, son of Alphaeus

These four are also numbered among Yeshuah's Twelve. Thomas is a sincere "I'll-believe-it-when-I-see-it" realist. Thaddaeus (also called Jude), Simon (known as "the Zealot" because of his extreme political views), and James (referred to as "son of Alphaeus" or "James the Less") do not enjoy the same high profile as the others, but nobody should doubt their loyalty to Yeshuah ...or should they?

James & John, the sons of Zebedee

James and his younger brother John are also fishermen. With Peter, they enjoy the closest relationship with Yeshuah, who calls them "Sons of Thunder" for their passion and enthusiasm. Yet there is some tension in the group because John may be Yeshuah's favorite. Will petty rivalry and jealousy break the Twelve apart?